K¹² Classics for Young Readers

Volume B

Book Staff and Contributors

Beth Zemble *Director, Alternative Learning Strategies; Director, English Language Arts*

Mary Beck Desmond *Senior Text Editor*

Suzanne Montazer *Creative Director, Print and ePublishing*

Jayoung Cho *Senior Visual Designer*

Oltjen Design Associates *Print Visual Designers*

Kim Barcas, Stephanie Shaw Williams *Cover Designers*

Amy Eward *Senior Manager, Writers*

Colleen Line *Senior Project Manager*

Maria Szalay *Senior Vice President for Product Development*

John Holdren *Senior Vice President for Content and Curriculum*

David Pelizzari *Vice President, Content and Curriculum*

Kim Barcas *Vice President, Creative*

Laura Seuschek *Vice President, Instructional Design and Evaluation & Studies*

Aaron Hall *Vice President, Program Management*

Lisa Dimaio Iekel *Production Manager*

John Agnone *Director of Publications*

Illustrations Credits

All illustrations © K12 unless otherwise noted

Bandelin-Dacey Studios, 1–3; Carolina Farías, 4–5; Yevgenia Nayberg, 6–13; John Manders, 14–21; Carolina Farías, 22–23; Sue Williams, 24–29; Peter Francis, 30–35; Donald Wu, 36–41; Tiphanie Beeke, 42–51; Mike Reed, 52–59; Jay Shin, 60–63; Donald Wu, 64–71; Bandelin-Dacey Studios, 72–79; John Manders, 80–87; Robert Meganck, 88–97; Carolina Farías, 98–103; Yevgenia Nayberg, 104–111; Carolina Farías, 112–117; Jay Shin, 118–119; Peter Francis, 120–121; Jay Shin, 122–123

About K12 Inc.

K12 Inc., a technology-based education company, is the nation's leading provider of proprietary curriculum and online education programs to students in grades K–12. K[12] provides its curriculum and academic services to online schools, traditional classrooms, blended school programs, and directly to families. K12 Inc. also operates the K[12] International Academy, an accredited, diploma-granting online private school serving students worldwide. K[12]'s mission is to provide any child the curriculum and tools to maximize success in life, regardless of geographic, financial, or demographic circumstances. K12 Inc. is accredited by CITA. More information can be found at www.K12.com.

13-digit: 978-1-60153-170--4
10-digit: 1-60153-170-2
Printed by RR Donnelley, Roanoke, VA, USA, April 2011, Lot 042011

Contents

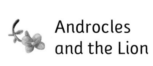 

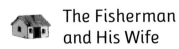 

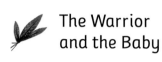 

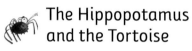 

K¹² Classics
for Young Readers

Volume B

The *Lion* and the **Fox**

A lion who was old and weak could not go out to hunt for food. He went into his den and made believe that he was very sick.

Many animals went into the den to look at him. When they came near, he caught them and ate them.

After a great many had been caught in this way, a fox came along. He sat down outside the den and asked the lion how he was.

The lion said that he was very sick, and he begged the fox to come in and see him.

"I would," said the fox, "but I notice that all the footprints point into your den, and that none point out."

The **Hound** and the **Hare**

A Hound startled a Hare near the woods and began to chase her. As the Hare ran back and forth, the Hound played a game. At first, he bit her with his teeth as if he would end her life. Then he tumbled her in the grass as if playing with another dog.

Finally, not knowing whether she would be eaten or be the Hound's friend, the Hare stopped running.

She said, "Hound, I wish you would act truthfully with me. If you are my friend, why do you bite me? And if you are my enemy, why do you play with me?"

The **Fox** and
the **Grapes**

One day, a very hungry Fox came walking on a road. He spied a lush grapevine. The vine had large bunches of pretty purple grapes hanging down.

"Oh, those big grapes will make a fine lunch," said the Fox. He tried jumping to reach them, but the grapes were too high. He tried climbing the grapevine, but he kept falling off.

Then the Fox took a stick in his mouth and tried to bat the grapes down, but he could not hit them.

Now the Fox was tired and still hungry. "Well," he said, "I'm sure those grapes were sour and not ripe, anyway." And he marched off in a huff.

The *Goose and* the **Golden Eggs**

There was once a man who had a goose. This goose was not like the geese you can find on a farm.

She was a very handsome goose, and every day she laid a big, golden egg.

The man sold the eggs at the market. He saved the money and was slowly getting rich.

One day, he said to himself, "I wish that I were rich now. Every day my goose lays a golden egg. She must have many golden eggs inside her. If she has not, how can she lay golden eggs? If I could have all the gold at once I should be very rich." So the man killed his goose and tried to find the gold.

Alas! There was no gold to be found. The foolish man had lost the good that he had, without getting the riches that he wished. ❧

The *The* **Pied Piper** *of* **Hamelin**

Hamelin is a little town in a country across the sea. Long ago, a strange thing happened in Hamelin. A great many rats came into the town.

They were big, fierce rats. They chased the cats and dogs and scared the children. They ate the food on the tables. They ran up and down the streets in the daytime.

The Wise Men tried to think of a way to drive

the rats out of the town. Cats and dogs could not do it, and the rats would not eat poison.

The Mayor said, "I wish I had a trap big and strong enough to catch the rats. I would give all my gold for it."

Just then there came a knock at the door. "Come in," said the Mayor.

The door opened and in came a very strange man. He was tall and thin, with bright blue eyes and light hair. His long coat was half of yellow and half of red. No one had ever seen him before.

The strange man went up to the Mayor and said, "I can drive the rats out of the town."

"Who are you," cried the Wise Men, "and how can you do this thing?"

"I am called the Pied Piper. I cannot tell you what I shall do. If you will promise to give me a thousand pieces of gold, I will soon show you."

"A thousand!" cried the Mayor. "I will give you five thousand if you can get rid of these rats!"

"No," said the Pied Piper, "a thousand is my fair price, and a thousand it shall be."

Then the Pied Piper went into the street. He took a pipe from his long coat and began to play a merry tune. Soon the rats came running from the houses.

> *Great rats, small rats, lean rats, brawny rats,*
> *Brown rats, black rats, gray rats, tawny rats,*
> *Grave old plodders, gay young friskers,*
> *Fathers, mothers, uncles, cousins,*
> *Cocking tails, and pricking whiskers,*
> *Families by tens and dozens,*
> *Brothers, sisters, husbands, wives—*
> *Followed the Piper for their lives.*

The Piper walked slowly down the street, playing a merry tune, and

THE PIED PIPER OF HAMELIN

the rats followed, dancing. They thought the music was about good things to eat. They forgot everything else as they ran after the Piper.

When they came to the river, every rat danced into the water and was swept away. How happy the people were! They rang the bells and shouted for joy.

Then the Pied Piper said to the Mayor, "Now, if you please, I will take my thousand pieces of gold."

"A thousand pieces of gold!" cried the Mayor.

"That is too much money. I will give you fifty."

"If you do not give me the money, you will be sorry," said the strange man.

"You can do us no harm," said the Mayor. "The rats are dead. You cannot bring them back."

Then the Pied Piper went into the street again. He played a few sweet notes on his pipe. At once the children came out of the houses.

All the little boys and girls,
With rosy cheeks and flowing curls,
And sparkling eyes and teeth like pearls,
Tripping and skipping ran merrily after
The wonderful music with shouting
and laughter.

The Piper walked down the street and through the fields. When he reached the foot of the hill, a door opened and he went in, still playing the beautiful tune.

All the children followed him and the door closed. One little boy, who was lame, could not run as fast as the other children. When

the Mayor and the Wise Men came running up, they found him crying.

"Why do you cry?" said the Mayor.

"I wished to go with the other children," he said. "When the man played on his pipe it told us about a beautiful land. The sun was shining and the birds were singing. The children played in the fields. They were never ill nor lame. I ran as fast as I could, but when I came the children were gone, and I could not find the door."

The Mayor sent men north, south, east, and west to find the Piper. He said, "Tell him that I will give him all the gold in the town if he will come back and bring the children with him."

The fathers and mothers of Hamelin waited and waited, but their little ones did not come back.

All this was long ago, but no one has ever seen the Piper or the little children since.

If you go to Hamelin, the people will show you the hill and the river. You may walk down Pied Piper Street, but you will hear no music. No one is allowed to sing or play a tune on the street down which the children followed the Pied Piper to the land beyond the hills. ཀྵ

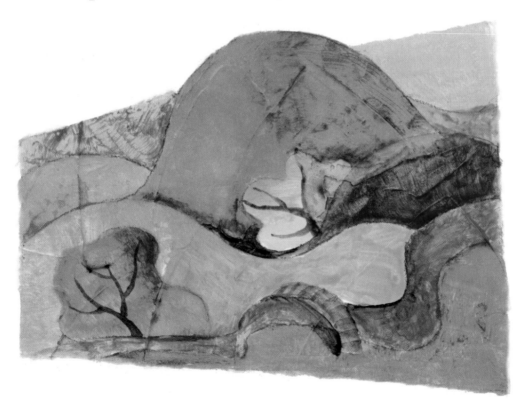

The Bremen Town Musicians

Once there was a poor Donkey. He had worked hard all his life. But he had grown very old and had become useless.

One day, he heard his master say that he was a useless old Donkey, and that he must be killed very soon.

"I'll not stay here to be killed," said the Donkey. "I'll run away."

So he jumped over the fence and went down the road till he met a Dog.

"Where are you going, Mr. Dog?" asked the Donkey.

"I have run away," said the Dog. "They say that I am too old to work, and that they will have me killed. I will not stay to be killed."

"Right! Right!" said the Donkey. "Come with me, my good friend. You and I will go to Bremen town, and we will play in the band. You can play the flute, and I can beat the drum."

So the Donkey and the Dog went on together. By and by, they met a Cat. "How do you do, Mrs. Puss?" said they. "Where are you going?"

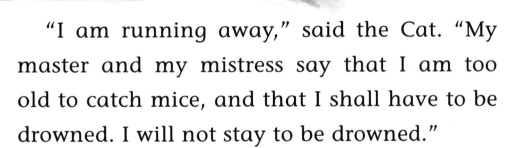

"I am running away," said the Cat. "My master and my mistress say that I am too old to catch mice, and that I shall have to be drowned. I will not stay to be drowned."

"Come with us," said the Donkey. "We are going to Bremen town to play in the band. You shall sing."

"That will suit me very well," said the Cat. So they all walked on.

By and by, the three came to a farm. There on a fence stood a Cock, crowing as loud as he could.

"What ails you?" asked the Donkey. "Why do you crow so loud?"

"The cook says that I must go into the soup pot," answered the Cock. "So I will crow while I can, and as loud as I like."

"Why not come with us?" said the Donkey. "We are going to Bremen town, to play in the band. You can sing beautifully. Come with us. What do you say?"

"I will join you," said the Cock. So they all went on together.

It was now quite dark, and the four began to look about for a place to spend the night. "Let us sleep under this tree," said the Donkey.

So the Donkey and the Dog lay down on the ground. The Cat climbed into the tree, and the Cock flew up to the top.

"I see a light," cried the Cock. "There is a house not far away."

"Let us ask the people for supper," said the Donkey.

"How good a bone would taste!" said the Dog.

"Or a fat mouse," said the Cat.

"Or some corn,"said the Cock.

They set out at once to the place where they saw the light. At last they reached the house. The Donkey, being the tallest, looked in the window.

"What do you see?" asked the others.

"I see a table with supper on it, and four robbers are eating and drinking."

"Come down," said the Dog, "and we will think of a way to get that supper."

So they thought of a plan to frighten the robbers away. And this is what they did.

The Donkey stood on his hind legs, and placed his forefeet on the windowsill.

The Dog climbed up and stood on the Donkey's back.

The Cat jumped up and stood on the Dog's back.

And the Cock flew up and stood on the Cat's back.

Then, all together, they began to make their loudest music.

The Donkey brayed, the Dog barked, the Cat mewed, the Cock crowed. They made such a noise that the robbers left their supper and ran away as fast as possible. Then the four friends sat down and ate the supper. "Now," said the Donkey, "let us all go to bed."

So the Donkey lay down in the yard, the Dog slept behind the door, the Cat curled up by the fire, and the Cock flew up on the roof. They were all so tired that they soon fell fast asleep.

About midnight, the robbers saw that the light was out, and that all was still. So one of them crept back to the house. As he went to the fire to strike a light, the Cat flew at him and scratched him with her long nails. This frightened him so much that he ran back to the door. As he passed by, the Dog bit him in the leg. As he ran through the yard, the Donkey kicked him so hard that he was flung into the road. All this woke the Cock, who cried with all his might, "Cock-a-doodle-doo!"

The robber ran back to his friends. "There was a wicked old witch sitting by the fire," he said. "She scratched me with her nails! Behind the door was a man. He had a long, sharp knife, and he stabbed me in the leg! In the yard was a giant who kicked me out into the road! And then there was somebody who kept calling and calling, 'Kill the robber, do! Kill the robber, do!'"

So the robbers went away again as far as they possibly could, for they were very much afraid. And the four friends stayed in the little house in the woods, and for all that you and I know, they are there now. ✒

Clytie

People long ago thought that gods and goddesses lived in the trees and brooks and flowers. One of the most beautiful of these goddesses was golden-haired Clytie.

Clytie was a water goddess that lived in a river near the great sea. She loved the sun god Apollo who drove the chariot of the sun.

Day after day, Clytie stood on the bank of her river home and watched for Apollo's chariot to come up in the east. All day, she stood and watched him driving across the sky. In the evening, when the sun went down, she stood looking after him.

For nine long days, she stood there. All that time, she ate nothing but dewdrops, and every day she grew paler and thinner.

At last the gods took pity on her. They changed her into a beautiful flower.

Her feet became roots in the ground. Her body changed to a green stem, and her golden hair turned to yellow petals.

But Clytie still kept her face turned toward Apollo as he crossed the sky. So it came to pass that people named her Sunflower.

Pandora's Box

A long time ago, there lived a maiden named Pandora. In those days, everyone was happy, for trouble and pain were not known.

Pandora should have been the happiest of all, for when she was born, the gods gave her all their gifts. She had health and good temper, and wit and beauty, and everything else that a maiden could wish.

But Pandora had one thing that did not make her happy. It was a beautiful wooden box tied with a golden cord. The king of the gods himself had given it to her.

"What good does it do me?" Pandora said to herself. "What good is a box tied up with a golden cord if you have been told never, never to open it?"

Now, Pandora wished and wished and wished that she could know what was in the box. Every day she sat looking at it and wondering what could be inside it.

"What harm could it do?" she said to herself. "I would only peep in and close the lid quickly."

Once she thought she heard soft noises inside. That time, she had her fingers on the cord. Then she suddenly remembered and stopped.

At last Pandora could stand it no longer, and she opened the box. She thought she would just lift the lid and close it again quickly.

But before she knew it, a swarm of ugly creatures flew out.

Then Pandora felt pain and sorrow for the first time in her life. With a cry, she dropped the lid of the box. But it was too late.

She had let loose the troubles of the world. They flew out through the window, carrying sorrow and pain everywhere.

Pandora was very much frightened. As she sat there wondering what she should do, she

heard a sweet voice inside the box. "Pandora," it called. "Pandora, let me out. I am Hope, and I will help you."

Now, Pandora did not know who Hope was, but the voice sounded so kind that she lifted the lid.

The little creature that came out this time was not a bit like the others. Her wings were like sunshine. It made Pandora feel better just to see her.

Of course, Hope could not bring the ugly creatures back into Pandora's box. They flew through the world, carrying pain and sorrow where such things had never before been known.

But wherever they went, Hope went, too, bringing comfort to all who were sick and sad. She is still in the world today, and happy are the people who have seen her wings. ꙮ

Echo

Long, long ago, there lived a young girl named Echo. She was very bright and pretty, but she was very naughty, too.

She dearly loved to tease. She teased her mother, she teased her father, and she teased her brothers and her sisters. She played tricks on all the people she knew.

"You like to tease too much," her friends would say to her. "Someday you will be sorry."

But Echo would only laugh and go on with her tricks.

One day, she was foolish enough to play a trick on the great Queen Juno. Queen Juno was very angry.

"After this, you shall never speak to anyone first," she said. "You shall only say again what others say to you."

Poor Echo! All her fun was gone. She could not speak to anyone, but could only answer when she was called.

She grew thinner and thinner, and weaker and weaker. At last she faded away until she was only a voice.

Sometimes you can hear her now in the woods. She will not speak to you, but she will answer you back if you call. ✑

Androcles
and the Lion

Androcles was a slave. He lived with his master in Rome, many years ago. The master was a cruel man. Androcles did not have enough to eat, and he had to work very hard.

One night, Androcles ran away. He crept along until he was outside the city walls. Then he ran until he was tired. He lay down on the soft grass and went to sleep. In the morning, he looked around and saw that he was near a forest. He knew there were wild animals in the forest, but he thought the animals would be no crueler to him than his master had been.

Androcles was very hungry. He ate some nuts and berries and drank some water from a spring. He found a dark cave in the rocks. He sat down in the cave and tried to plan what he would do next.

Suddenly, he saw a shadow across the low opening of the cave. He heard the roar of a wild animal. Androcles was a brave man, but the roar frightened him. He tried to run away, but the animal filled the low opening.

Then Androcles saw that it was a lion. The great lion raised one paw and moaned with pain. He had a thorn in the soft part of his paw.

Androcles had often taken thorns out of the paws of his master's dogs. So he gently took the lion's paw in his hand. The lion sat very still while the thorn was being pulled out. Then he did just what the dogs had done. He rolled over and over in his joy.

He licked the hands of Androcles and tried to lick his face.

When Androcles left the cave, the lion followed him. The lion was a good hunter and caught small game for him. They lived together in the cave and became good friends.

One day, Androcles left the cave and walked by himself in the forest. Suddenly, he was seized by soldiers from Rome. His cruel master had sent them to hunt for him. They took him

back to Rome. He was put into prison.

After many days, they took him out of prison. They took him to a large open place like a circus. There were seats on every side. The seats were full of cruel men and women. His master was there and his master's friends. They had come to see Androcles fight for his life with a hungry lion.

Androcles stood still, waiting for the lion. All the people watched and waited. The cage door was opened. Out rushed a hungry lion. Androcles was frightened but he did not move. On came the lion, but just as he reached Androcles, he stopped and sniffed the air. Then, with a joyous bound, he lay down at the feet of his old friend. Androcles stroked the

head of the lion. The lion licked the hands and feet of Androcles.

All the people watched. There was not a sound in the great place. Then a cheer went up as they saw that Androcles and the lion were friends.

"Tell us about it," the people cried. So Androcles told his story. Then he waited. He thought the cruel people might make him fight another lion. But the people did not feel cruel now.

"Let them both go free!" they shouted. So Androcles and the lion went back to the forest together. ❧

The *Jackals* and the **Lion**

Characters
LION
MOTHER JACKAL
FATHER JACKAL

LION: I am hungry. I must find something to eat for my dinner. Gr-r-r-r-r! Where can all the animals be? I shall look till I find one. Gr-r-r-r-r!

MOTHER JACKAL: Do you hear that lion roaring? I am afraid he will eat us today. He has eaten all the other animals in the forest, and now he is looking for us, I know.

FATHER JACKAL: Don't be afraid. I will take care of you. Let us run away from here. Come quick, quick, quick!

The two little jackals run here and there looking for a place to hide.

LION: Gr-r-r-r-r!

MOTHER JACKAL: Do you hear that roar again? I am so frightened. He will be sure to find us and kill us at once. What shall we do?

FATHER JACKAL: He will not find us. We will hide till he goes back to his den. Then we will go to see him and talk to him about it.

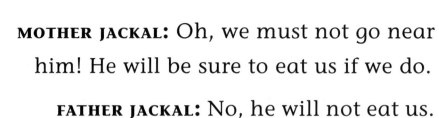

MOTHER JACKAL: Oh, we must not go near him! He will be sure to eat us if we do.

FATHER JACKAL: No, he will not eat us. I'll see to that. He is not roaring now, so he must have gone back to his den. Come, we will go to him, and I'll show you what we can do.

The two jackals go to the lion's den. The lion sees them coming and begins to roar.

LION: Who is this I see coming to my den? Gr-r-r-r-r-r! It is those two little jackals, and I have been hunting for them for three days. Gr-r-r-r-r! Where have you been hiding all the time? Didn't you know that I have been hunting for you? Come to me at once. I shall eat you for my dinner today.

FATHER JACKAL: O great Lion, we know we should have come to you sooner than this, but there is a much bigger lion than you in the forest. He tried to catch us and eat us, and we were so frightened we had to run away.

LION: What do you mean? There is no lion in this forest but me.

FATHER JACKAL: Oh, yes, there is. And he is much bigger and more terrible than you.

LION: That can't be true. Take me to this lion at once and I will take care of him.

FATHER JACKAL: Follow us, then, and we will take you to this terrible lion. See! That is where he lives. Look down into that well and you will see him. He looks like you.

The lion looks down into the well and thinks he sees another lion.

LION: What are you doing down there? I am the only lion that has any right in this forest. Come out of there!

Gr-r-r-r-r! Come out, I say! If you do not come out, I shall jump down there and that shall be the end of you.

The lion jumps down into the well. Soon he begins to roar. The jackals peep into the well.

JACKALS: Ho ho! Old lion! It was only yourself that you saw in the well. You may roar all you please, but you can't eat any more little jackals. ❧

The *Ugly* Duckling

Hans Christian Andersen

It was beautiful out in the country. It was summer. The cornfields were yellow and the oats were green. The hay was put up in stacks in the green meadows. Yes, it was beautiful out in the country.

A duck sat in her nest under the bushes. There were eggs in the nest, and she must hatch her young ones. At last one eggshell cracked, and then another. "Peep! Peep!" said the little ducks as they came out of the eggshells.

They looked all around them under the green leaves. The mother duck stood up and looked at her ducklings. Then she looked in the nest. There lay the largest egg of all. "How long must I sit here?" said the duck. "I am tired." But she sat down again.

"How are your ducklings?" asked an old duck who came to visit her.

"Look at them. Are they not the prettiest ducklings that you ever saw? They are all out but one. This egg will not crack."

"Let me see the egg," said the duck. "I think that it is a turkey's egg. Let it lie there, and teach your other children to swim."

"I think that I will sit on it a little longer," said the mother.

"As you please," said the old duck, and she went away.

At last the big egg cracked. "Peep! Peep!" said the little one as he came out of the shell. He was very large and very ugly.

The mother looked at him. "He does not look like the others," said she. "Can he be a turkey? We shall see. He must go into the water even if I have to push him in myself."

The next day was bright and sunny. The mother duck went to the pond with her little ones. Splash! She jumped into the water. "Quack! Quack!" she said, and all the duck- lings followed her. They swam about in the water. The ugly duckling swam with them.

"No, he is not a turkey," thought the mother. "How well he can swim! He is my own child."

"Quack! Quack!" she said. "Come with me to the farmyard. Keep near me and do not let the cat catch you."

So they came to the farmyard, and all the other ducks looked at them. "See that ugly duckling! We will not have him here," said one duck, and she flew up and bit him in the neck.

"Let him alone," said the mother. "He did not hurt you."

"Yes, but he is so large and ugly," said the duck who had bitten him.

"Your other children are very pretty," said the old duck. "Make yourself at home."

Now they were at home, but the duckling that came out of the big egg was bitten and laughed at by the ducks and chickens. "He is too big," they said.

The poor duckling was sad because he looked so ugly. At last he ran and hid in the bushes.

The little birds saw him and were afraid of him. "That is

because I am so ugly," he thought. So he shut his eyes and flew far away over the fields.

At night, the duckling came to a little hut. The door was open, and he went into the room. A poor woman lived in the hut with her cat and her hen. In the morning, when they saw the duckling, the cat began to purr and the hen began to cluck.

"What is this?" said the woman. She could not see well and she thought it was a fat duck.

THE UGLY DUCKLING

"Now," she said, "I shall have duck's eggs."

So the duckling lived in the hut for three weeks, but no eggs came.

"Can you lay eggs?" asked the hen.

"No."

"Then do not talk to me," said the hen.

"Can you purr?" asked the cat.

"No."

"Then do not talk to me," said the cat.

At last one morning the duckling saw the sunshine and wished to swim on the water. He told this wish to the hen.

"What are you thinking of?" cried the hen. "You have nothing to do. That is why you think of such things. Purr, or lay eggs, and forget your silly wishes."

"But it is such fun to swim," said the duckling. "I like to put my head into the water and dive to the bottom of the pond."

"Yes, it must be fun!" said the hen. "What are you thinking of? Ask the cat about it. Ask him if he likes to swim, or to dive into the water."

"You do not understand me," said the duckling. "I think that I will fly out into the world again."

"Yes, do go," said the hen.

The duckling flew away to the water. He swam and dived, but he was not happy. No one liked him because he was so ugly.

Now came the autumn. The leaves in the forest turned yellow and brown. The wind played with them, and they danced over the ground.

One evening, some beautiful birds came out of the bushes. They were as white as snow. They were swans. They flew high in the air and sailed away to the warm South.

The ugly duckling watched them. He did not know their names, but he loved them because they were so beautiful.

The winter was very, very cold. The poor duckling lived in the woods near the pond. He was often cold and hungry. It would be too sad if I were to tell you how unhappy he was.

At last spring came. The warm sun shone and the birds began to sing. Then all at once the duckling could flap his wings. He flew high in the air and far away over fields and meadows. At last he came to a river in a beautiful garden. Three swans were swimming on the water.

"I will fly to them," said the duckling, "and they will kill me because I am so ugly. But what of that! It is better to be killed by them than to be bitten by the ducks and chickens in the farmyard."

So he flew into the water and swam toward the beautiful swans. They looked at him and came sailing down the river.

"Kill me," said the poor duckling, and he bent his head upon the water.

But what was this that he saw in the water! It was his own image. He was not an ugly duckling now. He was a beautiful white swan.

Some children came into the garden and threw bread and corn into the water. "There is a new swan!" cried one of the little girls.

The other children said, "Yes, a new one has come, and he is the most beautiful of all."

The old swans bowed their heads to him. Then the young swan hid his head under his wing, for he did not know what to do. He had always been called ugly, and now he heard the children say that he was beautiful.

"I never dreamed of being so happy," he thought, "while I was an ugly duckling."

The **Grasshopper** and the **Ant**

Characters
GRASSHOPPER
ANT

Scene 1 — Summer
A PLEASANT FIELD

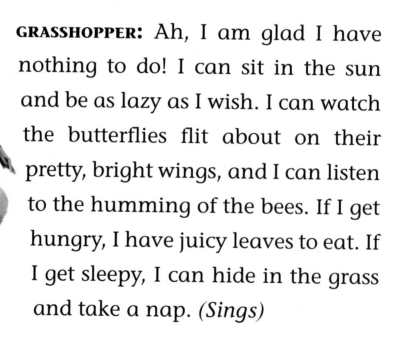

GRASSHOPPER: Ah, I am glad I have nothing to do! I can sit in the sun and be as lazy as I wish. I can watch the butterflies flit about on their pretty, bright wings, and I can listen to the humming of the bees. If I get hungry, I have juicy leaves to eat. If I get sleepy, I can hide in the grass and take a nap. *(Sings)*

The summertime's the time for me,
For then I'm happy as can be.
I watch the butterflies and bees;
I smoke my pipe and take my ease.

I do no work the livelong day;
I pass the time in fun and play.
Oh, summertime's the time for me!
For then I'm happy as can be.

An ant comes along.

Hello, Mr. Ant! Where are you going so fast?

ANT: About my work, of course. I'm a busy ant, I am.

GRASSHOPPER: Oh, you are, are you? Well, you needn't be so cross about it.

ANT: Did I speak crossly? I didn't mean to. I'm sorry. But I am very busy and can't stop to talk. (*Starts to go*)

GRASSHOPPER: Wait, wait! You can take time to talk a minute, can't you?

ANT: Why, yes, if you really have something to say.

GRASSHOPPER: Ha, ha! You make me laugh. Can't you stop a while to talk with your friends, even if they haven't much to say?

ANT: I have no time to waste.

GRASSHOPPER: Why, what are you doing today?

ANT: I am very busy getting ready for winter.

GRASSHOPPER: Getting ready for winter! Why, winter is a long way off!

ANT: It will be here soon enough.

GRASSHOPPER: Well, I don't see why you don't have a good time while you can.

ANT: But if I don't gather food for the winter now, while there is plenty of it, I shall not have anything to eat when cold weather comes.

GRASSHOPPER: Oh, you are a dull fellow! You have no fun in you.

ANT: I don't work all the time. I am busy all day, but when evening comes, I sit at home and talk with my friends.

GRASSHOPPER: Well, I don't mean to work at all in this fine weather. I'm going to have a good time.

ANT: Wait till winter comes, and we shall see who is wiser—you or I. Good-bye, I have work to do. *(Goes on)*

GRASSHOPPER: What a foolish fellow that ant is! He does nothing but work, work, work. He doesn't have any fun at all. Well, I don't care. I am going to have a good time. *(Sings)*

The summertime's the time for me,
For then I'm happy as can be.
I hop about among the flowers;
I sing and dance for hours and hours.
I care not what the ant may say;
The summertime's the time for play.
Oh, summertime's the time for me!
For then I'm happy as can be.

Scene 2 — Winter
IN FRONT OF THE ANT'S HOUSE

ANT: *(Looking out of the window)* Ah, it's a cold day! I'm glad I don't have to go out. I can stay cozily at home and talk with my friends. I have plenty of food, too, so I have nothing to do through the winter but have a good time.

Grasshopper comes along. He looks thin and hungry. His clothes are old and ragged. He stops in front of the ant's house.

GRASSHOPPER: Oh, Mr. Ant, won't you please give me something to eat?

ANT: Why, Mr. Grasshopper, is that you? I hardly knew you. You are not looking very well.

GRASSHOPPER: No, no! I'm afraid not. I'm not feeling well, either.

ANT: Why, what's the matter?

GRASSHOPPER: I am hungry. Won't you please give me something to eat?

ANT: Something to eat! Why, what did you do all summer?

GRASSHOPPER: I sang and played all summer. I had plenty of food then. Now it is cold, and there is nothing to eat.

ANT: Oh, you lazy fellow! You sang and played all summer, while the rest of us were busy storing up food for the winter. Now that it is cold and there is no food, you ask us to feed you. Take this grain, but do not ask again. You shall get no more from me.

GRASSHOPPER: Ah, me! Why did I not work as the ant did, and store up food while there was still food to get? *(Sings sadly)*

> *I did no work all summer long.*
> *And now I know that I was wrong.*
> *It isn't right for me to play*
> *While the ants work hard all day.*
> *Next time I'll work as well as dance,*
> *Then I'll be ready, like the ants.* ❧

The *Three* Wishes

There was once a poor woodcutter who worked all day in the forest. He gathered great bundles of sticks and sold them in the village.

Once he had very bad luck indeed. No one wanted to buy any of his sticks. When the night came, he had not a cent to take home to his wife.

"Dear me!" said the poor woodcutter. "No supper for us tonight!"

Just then he heard a strange noise in the dead leaves near the path. He turned to look and saw a rabbit caught in a trap.

"Here is supper," cried the old man, and ran to the trap.

"If you spare me," cried the rabbit, "I will grant the first three wishes made by you or your good wife."

"That is better than one supper," said the woodcutter, and he opened the trap.

The rabbit ran off into the forest, and the happy woodcutter hurried home to tell the good news to his wife.

She met him at the door of the hut. "What have you brought for supper?" she said.

"Nothing!" said the old man.

"Then there is nothing at all to eat," she wailed. "Oh, I wish I had a cake as big as a cart wheel!"

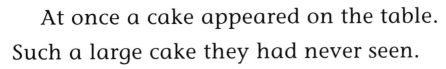

At once a cake appeared on the table. Such a large cake they had never seen.

"Wife, wife! What have you done?" cried the man. "We had three wishes. You have used one of them for a cake. I wish it were hung from your nose."

As he spoke, the cake rose slowly and stuck to the old woman's nose. The poor woodcutter was surprised. He pulled, but the cake stuck fast.

"Oh dear! Oh dear! Take it away!" cried the woman, but there it stayed.

"Never mind," said the woodcutter. "We have one more wish. Let us ask for all the riches in the world."

"But my nose!" cried the woman. "What is gold to me, while I have this great cake on my nose?"

"Hush!" cried the old woodcutter, but his wife would not hush.

Then the woodcutter became angry. "Away with the cake!" he shouted. "I wish it would fly up the chimney!"

Before the old man had said it, the big cake rolled from its place, and then flew up the chimney. A few crumbs rattled in the ashes, and that was the end of the three wishes. ❧

The *Foolish* Goose

Characters
GRAY GOOSE
WISE OLD CROW
WHITE CRANE
BROWNIE HEN
A FARMER

Time: ONE BRIGHT MORNING   **Place:** A BIG ROAD

Gray Goose goes walking down the road, with a bag of corn—very proud and happy. He meets Wise Old Crow.

WISE OLD CROW: Good morning, Gray Goose! What a heavy bag you have there! It is too much for you to carry alone. Let me help you.

GRAY GOOSE: Oh, no! It is a big bag of corn, but I can carry it without any help.

WISE OLD CROW: Oh, well, I just wanted to help you as a friend. How long do you think your bag of corn will last you? I can tell

you of a plan to make a little corn go a
long way.

GRAY GOOSE: What is your plan? Tell me how to
make my corn go a long way, Wise Old Crow.

He puts down his bag of corn in the road.

WISE OLD CROW: First, you must spread your corn
out on the ground, so that we can count it.
Then, you count on one side and I will count
on the other side.

Gray Goose takes some of the corn out of the bag and spreads it on the ground.

GRAY GOOSE: *(Counting)* One, two, three, four, five, six, seven, eight, nine—

WISE OLD CROW: *(Eating a grain of corn each time he counts)* One, two, three, four, five, six, seven, eight, nine—

GRAY GOOSE: *(Looking up)* What are you doing, Wise Old Crow? Stop eating my corn!

WISE OLD CROW: *(As he flies away, laughing)* Caw! Caw! Caw! I told you that I knew a plan to make a little corn go a long way!

Gray Goose picks up his bag of corn, which is not so heavy now, and goes along the road. After a while, he meets White Crane.

WHITE CRANE: Good morning, Gray Goose! What do you have in your bag?

GRAY GOOSE: Oh, that is some of the best corn in the world.

WHITE CRANE: Is that all? You carry it with such care that I thought it must be pearls or diamonds.

GRAY GOOSE: No, I've never seen any pearls or diamonds. I should like very much to see such sights!

WHITE CRANE: Well, just swim out to that big rock in the lake over there. The bottom of the lake is covered with beautiful pearls and diamonds. I will keep your corn for you.

Gray Goose swims out to see the wonderful sights. While he is gone, White Crane eats nearly all of the corn. Gray Goose cannot see any pearls or diamonds on the bottom of the lake. When he starts back, he sees White Crane eating the corn.

THE FOOLISH GOOSE

GRAY GOOSE: Go away from my corn, White Crane! Go away from my corn!

WHITE CRANE: *(As he flies off, laughing)* I told you that I would keep your corn for you, Gray Goose!

Gray Goose picks up the little corn that is left, and goes down the road. After a while, he meets Brownie Hen and her ten chicks.

BROWNIE HEN: What have you got in that little bag, Gray Goose?

GRAY GOOSE: Oh, just a few grains of corn. I had a big bagful, but White Crane ate most of it while I was looking for pearls and diamonds! I like to see strange sights.

BROWNIE HEN: Well, if you like to see strange sights, throw your corn upon the road and see what happens.

GRAY GOOSE: No, indeed! I know well enough what would happen! Your ten little chicks would eat every grain of it.

BROWNIE HEN: No, no, Gray Goose! My chicks will not steal your corn. Throw some of it upon the road. If my little ones eat a single grain, I will give you ten white eggs.

GRAY GOOSE: All right! I agree to that.

He throws down some corn. The chicks run toward it. But before they can eat it, Brownie Hen makes a noise like a hawk. The chicks run away, and Brownie Hen eats the corn.

BROWNIE HEN: I told you that my chicks would not eat your corn, Gray Goose!

Gray Goose goes on until he meets a Farmer.

FARMER: What is in your bag, Gray Goose?

GRAY GOOSE: *(Sadly)* Only a few grains of corn. My bag grows smaller and smaller. I wish I could make it grow bigger and bigger!

FARMER: Why don't you put the corn in the ground? Then it will grow, and you will always have plenty to eat.

GRAY GOOSE: I will do as you say, Farmer.

He plants it, and later the corn begins to grow. For every grain he planted, Gray Goose has hundreds of grains!

GRAY GOOSE: At last I have found a way to make my bag of corn grow bigger and bigger instead of smaller and smaller! ❧

Puss *in* Boots

A poor miller had three sons. When he died, he left them all he had. To the oldest, he left his mill. To the second, he left his donkey. To the youngest, he left his cat.

"What shall I do?" said the youngest. "My brothers can get on very well. They have the mill and the donkey. But I have only the cat. I wish I had silver and land."

But the cat purred and said, "Do not be sad, master. We shall do very well. Bring me a pair of boots to keep my feet from mud and briars, and get me a bag to carry. Then we'll see what can be done to get silver and land."

So he brought some fine large boots for his cat and a green

bag with a red string to close it. Then Puss took the bag and some apples, and marched out among the briars. She put a red apple into the bag, and left it open on the ground. Then she lay down and made believe that she was asleep.

Soon a young rabbit came to the place. It smelled the apple and looked into the bag. Then it went in to get the apple.

Puss pulled the string and shut the bag. She took the rabbit to the King of the country, and said, "My master is the Marquis of Carabas. He sends you this rabbit."

The King took the rabbit and said, "Tell your master I am much pleased."

Then Puss went into a field of corn, and sat with the bag open. Soon two young quails ran into it. Puss pulled the string and shut them in. She took these to the King, and said, "My master, the Marquis of Carabas, sends you these quails."

The King said, "Tell your master I am much pleased."

Every day for a month or more Puss took the King a present. And the King said every day, "Tell your master I am much pleased to receive this present."

One day, Puss heard the King say he would go riding by the river. She told her master to go and swim in the river.

Soon the King rode by with a company of men. Puss went to meet him along the bank of the river and called, "Help! Help! My master will drown."

The King sent his men to help. They drew the young man to the bank.

"This is the Marquis," said Puss. The King liked the young man. He thanked him for all the presents, and told his men to bring dry clothes for the Marquis. Then the King asked the Marquis to ride in the coach between himself and his daughter.

Puss marched on before, in her boots. Soon she saw some men cutting grass. She spoke to them and said, "Tell the King that this land belongs to the rich Marquis of Carabas."

So when the King came near and asked, "Whose land is this?" they answered, "This is part of the land of the Marquis of Carabas. He is very rich."

Puss walked on before, in her boots. Soon she came to a giant's castle. She stepped in. She saw the giant. He was big and mean and terrible. She said, "They say you can change yourself into a lion, or a mouse, or anything. I do not think it is true. Can you show me?"

"Yes," said the angry giant, "I will show you that I can." Then he changed himself into a lion, and roared so loud that he almost broke the windows. Puss was so frightened that she ran clear up to the roof.

When she came down and peeped into the room, there sat the giant. "That was wonderful," said Puss. "They say you can change yourself into little things as small as a rat or a mouse. I do not think it is true. Can you show me?"

"Yes," roared the giant, "I can show you!" Then he changed himself into a mouse. And what do you think Puss did? Zip! She jumped on the mouse and ate him up, just like that.

Then she went to meet the King, and said, "Oh King, this is the castle of the rich Marquis of Carabas."

The King was pleased with the castle and with the land and with the young Marquis. "This young man is a fine man to wed my daughter," said the King.

The King's daughter was happy to hear this, for she liked the young man very much.

So they were wed. The King stayed on a whole week at the castle. And Puss, and the master, and his wife were happy there ever after.

Tug-of-War

Turtle liked to boast and brag. For such a small animal, he had a very big opinion of himself. He even claimed to be as powerful as the biggest animals, Elephant and Hippopotamus.

One day he said, "When Elephant and Hippopotamus see me, they treat me with respect. They call me 'friend.' We are equals."

When Elephant and Hippopotamus heard this boast, they laughed. "Does Turtle say we call him 'friend'? That is nonsense. We are much bigger and more powerful than Turtle. We do not call him 'friend.' We have no time to waste thinking of so small a creature."

The animals told Turtle what Elephant and Hippopotamus said. "So," said Turtle, "because they are so much bigger, they think they are so much better. But I will show them that I am their equal. Just wait and see. They will call me 'friend,' indeed they will!" And he set off down the path.

Soon Turtle found Elephant lying among the trees. Elephant was himself almost as big as the trees. But Turtle walked right up to him and shouted, "Hey! Wake up and pay your respects to your friend."

Elephant looked around to see who was speaking. Then he saw Turtle. "What do you want, you little thing of no importance?" he groaned.

"Is that any way to speak to your friend?" snapped Turtle.

"I am not your friend, Turtle," replied Elephant. "I have heard that you have been boasting that Hippopotamus and I call you 'friend.' You have been saying that you are our equal. But we do not call you 'friend.' And you are not our equal. You are a foolish little creature. Be off with you."

"Listen to me, Elephant," said Turtle. "Because I am so small, and you are so big, you think that you are greater. But I say we are equal. And I say, let us have a contest to prove it. I challenge you to a tug-of-war."

Elephant laughed so hard that the ground shook. "A tug-of-war with you?" he roared. "Turtle, don't

be a stupid little crea-
ture. You would have no
chance against me."

"So, what have you
got to lose?" asked Turtle.
Then he cut a very long
vine and gave one end to
Elephant. "You take this
end. I will walk off with
the other end. Then we
will begin to pull. If you pull me down, you are
greater. If I pull you down, I am greater. We will
not stop to eat or sleep until one of us pulls the
other down, or until the vine breaks. And if the
vine breaks, we are equals, and you must call
me 'friend.'"

Turtle took the other end of the long vine and
walked far away until he came to the river. There
was Hippopotamus splashing in the water.

"Hey, friend! Come out!" shouted Turtle. "I
have something to say to you."

Hippopotamus came to the shore and snorted, "You are no friend of mine! You are a little good-for-nothing. Be off with you."

Then Turtle challenged Hippopotamus to a tug-of-war. "Take this vine," he said. "If you pull me down, you are greater. If I pull you down, I am greater. We will not stop to eat or sleep until one of us pulls the other down, or until the vine breaks. And if the vine breaks, we are equals, and you must call me 'friend.'"

"Turtle," said Hippopotamus, "I will do this only to stop your boasting, and to show you who is truly greater. Now go pick up your end of the vine and let us be done with it."

So Turtle walked till he came to the middle of the vine. He picked it up and gave it a very hard shake. Elephant felt this and started to tug. Hippopotamus felt the tug and started to tug back.

Elephant and Hippopotamus pulled with all their strength. The vine stretched tight. Turtle sat down on soft moss and watched the vine. It moved a few inches one way, then a few inches the other way. But neither Elephant nor Hippopotamus could pull the other down.

Turtle munched on some mushrooms for a snack. Then he fell asleep. He awoke refreshed from his nap to see the vine still pulled tight. He yawned and stretched. Then he walked up to the vine and cut it with a sharp rock. At either end, Elephant and Hippopotamus crashed hard to the ground.

Turtle went to see Elephant first. Elephant was rubbing his head. "I bumped my head when the vine broke," moaned Elephant.

"Oh," said Turtle, "I am so sorry, my friend."

"Yes, we will call each other 'friend,'" said Elephant. "You are small, but you are much stronger than I ever thought possible. We are equals."

Then Turtle went to see Hippopotamus, who was rubbing his leg. "So, Turtle," said Hippopotamus, "I see we are equals after all. Although I pulled with all my might, I could not pull you down. You amaze me, my little friend."

"Thank you, my friend," said Turtle.

And so it is that, whenever the animals hold a meeting, Turtle, Elephant, and Hippopotamus sit at the front and they call each other "friend." Now they rule as equals—but do you think they are equal? ❧

The *Fisherman*
and **His Wife**

A fisherman and his wife lived in a little old house by the sea. Every day the fisherman went down to the sea to fish. Every day his wife cooked the fish for dinner. One day, when he threw in his line, it suddenly became very heavy. He pulled and pulled, and out flopped a big fish. The fisherman said to himself, "This is too big for my wife and me. We will invite our friends to dinner."

But the fish said, "Oh, do not eat me. Put me back into the sea, and you shall have whatever you wish."

The fisherman quickly threw the fish back into the sea. "Who would eat a talking fish!" he said. "Go back to your friends, and I will throw my line for another fish." When he went back to his house, he told his wife about the talking fish.

"What a goose you are!" she said angrily. "Why did you not ask for something? Go back and ask him to change this shabby old house into a pretty cottage."

The fisherman walked slowly back to the sea. The water looked all yellow and green. The fisherman called:

"Oh, Man of the Sea,
Come listen to me,
For Ilsa, my wife,
The plague of my life,
Hath sent me to ask a gift
Of thee!"

The fish came swimming up to him.

"My wife wishes to live in a pretty little cottage," said the fisherman.

"Go home," said the fish. "She is in the cottage already."

The fisherman went home. Sure enough, there was his wife standing at the door of a pretty little cottage. The fisherman could hardly believe his eyes. There was a little garden in front and a chicken yard at the back.

"Ah! Now you shall be happy," said the fisherman.

And she was happy—for a week.

Then one day the wife said, "Husband, I am tired of this little cottage. It is too small. I wish to live in a big stone castle. Go to the fish and ask for one."

The fisherman walked slowly down to the sea. The water was dark and the sun did not shine.

The fisherman called:

"Oh, Man of the Sea,
Come listen to me,
For Ilsa, my wife,
The plague of my life,
Hath sent me to ask a gift
Of thee!"

The fish came swimming up to him.

"My wife wishes to live in a big stone castle," said the fisherman.

"Go home," said the fish. "She is in the castle already."

The fisherman went home. Sure enough, there was a great stone castle. When the fisherman came to the door, it was opened by a servant, who made a low bow. Inside the castle, he found more servants. And in the great hall he saw his wife. She was walking up and down, with her head in the air.

The fisherman rubbed his eyes and looked again. He saw golden chairs and tables and fine things to eat. He thought it must all be a dream.

"Wake up!" said his wife. "What are you staring at?"

"How grand it is!" said the fisherman. "Now you will be happy."

And happy she was—for a day.

The next morning, before the sun was up, Ilsa called to the fisherman, "Husband, go to the fish at once and tell him I wish to be queen of all the land."

The fisherman walked very slowly to the sea. The water was black and the waves rolled high. He called in a loud voice:

> *"Oh, Man of the Sea,*
> *Come listen to me,*
> *For Ilsa, my wife,*
> *The plague of my life,*
> *Hath sent me to ask a gift*
> *Of thee!"*

When the fish came swimming up to him, the fisherman said, "My wife desires to be queen of all the land."

"She is already queen," said the fish.

The fisherman hurried home and found his wife on a throne of gold and diamonds. She had a golden crown on her head, and wore a silk dress with a long train.

"Wife, wife, now you shall be happy," he said.

And happy she was—for an hour.

Then she said, "I am queen and you must do as I wish. I order you to go to the fish and tell him that I desire the power to make the sun and the moon rise and set whenever I choose."

The fisherman was very sad as he walked to the sea. The sky was full of black clouds. The waves were as high as hills. The thunder crashed and the fisherman had to shout:

"Oh, Man of the Sea,
Come listen to me,
For Ilsa, my wife,
The plague of my life,
Hath sent me to ask a gift
Of thee!"

The fish rose on the top of a wave.

The fisherman said, "My wife wishes the power to make the sun and moon rise and set whenever she chooses."

"Go to your little old house," said the fish. "Remain there and be content."

And there you will find the fisherman and his wife to this very day. ⌘

The *Warrior* and the *Baby*

In a village near the mountains lived a brave warrior. He had fought in many battles. In the hunt, he had faced many wild animals without fear. Everybody admired the brave warrior. The villagers said there was no one like him anywhere.

But then the warrior began to grow vain. He thought he was the greatest warrior in the world.

"No one can beat me," he boasted.

A wise old woman lived in the village. When she heard the warrior boasting, she smiled. "He is brave," she said. "But there is someone mightier in our village."

The warrior went to speak with the wise old woman. "Old Grandmother," he said, for that was what the villagers called her, "who is this person you speak of?"

"His name is Wah-sis," said the wise woman.

"And where is he, Old Grandmother?" said the warrior.

"He is there," said the wise woman. She pointed behind her.

There sat a plump little baby. The baby smiled and sucked on a piece of maple sugar. The warrior had no wife. He knew nothing about babies. But like all vain people, he thought he knew everything. The warrior laughed. "Old Grandmother, this is a joke," he said. "Anyone can see that I am mightier than this little baby."

The wise old woman smiled. She said, "If you are mightier than Wah-sis, then you can make him obey you."

"Of course!" said the warrior. "All the villagers obey me."

Then the warrior spoke to little Wah-sis. "Baby, come to me!" But the baby did not move.

He sat and sucked on his maple sugar. The warrior was surprised. The villagers always did what he told them to do. So the warrior spoke again to little Wah-sis. "Baby, come to me!" The baby smiled and sucked his maple sugar.

The warrior was amazed. No one had ever dared to disobey him. He grew angry. He frowned at little Wah-sis. Then he roared, "BABY, COME TO ME!" Little Wah-sis began to cry. The baby howled! The warrior had never

heard such sounds. He did not know what to do. But he knew he must try to stop the noise.

The warrior began to sing. Then he danced for the baby. Little Wah-sis began to smile. With his big round eyes, the baby watched the warrior dancing. Little Wah-sis thought it was all very funny. He smiled as he sucked on his maple sugar.

The warrior danced and danced. The sweat ran down his face. Then he grew tired and sat down. When the warrior sat, the baby cried and howled again.

Up jumped the warrior and danced again. Little Wah-sis smiled. The warrior danced until he was too tired to dance any longer.

The wise old woman spoke. "Did I not say that Wah-sis is mightier than you? No one is mightier than the baby. Everybody loves him and all obey him."

"It is true," sighed the warrior. As the tired warrior walked away, little Wah-sis smiled and sucked on his maple sugar. ✿

Rumplestiltskin

A miller had one daughter, of whom he was very proud. One day, he boasted to the king that she could spin straw into gold.

"Send the girl to the palace at once. I should like to try her skill," ordered the king.

The daughter of the miller was sent to the king's palace. The king led the frightened girl into a large room filled with straw. Then he gave her a spinning wheel.

"You shall spin all night," said he. "If you do not spin all this straw into fine gold, you shall surely die tomorrow morning."

The king closed the door and left the miller's daughter alone in the room. The poor girl began to cry. "Oh, dear father," she cried, "why did you ever boast that I could spin straw into gold? Is there no help for me?"

Suddenly, the door opened. A little elf with a hat walked into the room. "What does this mean?" he said.

"The king has ordered me to spin all this straw into gold, and I do not know how," the miller's daughter replied.

"What will you give me if I do it for you?" asked the elf.

"I will give you my necklace," said the miller's daughter.

The elf took the necklace. Then he seated himself at the wheel and worked busily all night.

Before sunrise, the king returned. The straw had been spun into gold. The king took all of it, but he wished to have still more. The next night, the king led the girl to a larger room filled with straw. Once more, he gave her a spinning wheel.

"Spin this straw into gold," he said, "or you shall die tomorrow morning." The king closed the door behind him, and the miller's daughter began to cry. At once the door opened, and the elf appeared.

"What will you give me this time if I spin the straw into gold?" the elf asked.

"I will give you my new ring," said the miller's daughter.

In the morning, the king was happy when he saw the shining gold, but he wanted still more. That very night, he led the poor girl to an even larger room filled with straw. "If you spin the straw into gold, you shall be my queen," he said. Then he left her alone in the room.

Again the little elf appeared. "If I spin all this straw into gold, what will you give me?" he said.

"I have nothing left to give you," the girl answered softly.

"Then promise, after you are queen, to give me your first child."

The girl did not know what to say. At last she said, "I will."

Again the straw was spun into gold, and on the very next day, the daughter of the miller married the king.

Years passed, and she was so happy that she forgot her promise to the elf.

One day, she was holding her baby when the old elf appeared in the room. Then she remembered.

"Oh, I cannot!" the poor queen cried. "I cannot part with my dear baby!"

"Guess my name," said the little elf, "and I will not take your child."

Then the queen sent her servants everywhere, to seek for strange names, but they could not find the right one.

One night, as a page was walking through a forest, he saw a small fire burning brightly. An elf was dancing around the fire, and as he danced, he sang:

"Today I bake;
Tomorrow I brew;
Then, little prince,
I come for you!
For no one knows,
Though great my fame,
That Rumpelstiltskin
Is my name!"

The page ran back and told the queen.

"I am sure that is the same elf," said the queen.

The elf came to the palace two days later. "If you do not guess my name today, I will take your baby," he said.

"You cannot take him," the queen said. "Your name is Rumpelstiltskin."

Then the elf was very, very angry. He tore his hair and stamped upon the ground so hard that his feet stuck fast. "A fairy told you that!" he cried.

The queen laughed and went away. The elf tried to follow her. He pulled and pulled, but there he stuck. There are some who say he stands there still. ꙮ

The **Hippopotamus**
and the **Tortoise**

Many years ago, a large, fat hippopotamus was the big king on land. He was second only to the mighty elephant. The hippo lived with his seven large, fat sisters. He loved his sisters, and he loved being king.

The hippo liked to give big feasts. He invited many other animals. They all came to his feasts. They all knew him. But no one knew his name. Only the hippo's seven sisters knew that he was called "Isantim."

One day, the hippo prepared a big feast. He invited all the animals. Just as they were about to sit down, the hippo said, "Wait! You have come to eat at my table. But do you know my name? If no one can tell me my name, you must all go away without any dinner."

No one could guess the hippo's name, so everyone had to go away. They had to leave all the good food. But before they left, the tortoise stood up.

He asked the hippo, "What if I tell you your name at the next feast? What would you do?"

The hippo replied, "I would be ashamed of myself. I would be so ashamed that I would take my whole family and leave the land forever. Then we would live in the water."

The next day, the tortoise watched the hippo and his seven sisters. He saw that they went to the river in the morning and in the evening to wash and have a drink. The hippo walked in front. His seven sisters followed him. They all walked on the same path.

The next day, the tortoise went to the path. He dug a small hole. Then he hid behind some tall grass and waited. Before long, the hippo and his sisters went down to the river. Soon, they came back. But two of the sisters were lagging behind.

The tortoise saw his chance. He hurried to the hole in the path. He buried himself in the hole. He hid his whole body. Only his shell was sticking up.

Soon, the last two hippo sisters came along. One of them tripped on the tortoise's shell.

"Ouch!" she cried. "Isantim, my brother! Help me! I have hurt my foot."

Now the tortoise knew the hippo's name. He crawled away and went home. He felt very happy.

Before the next feast started, the hippo again said to the animals, "Do you know my name? If no one can tell me my name, you must all go away without any dinner."

Then the tortoise got up. He shouted as loud as he could, "Your name is Isantim!" A great cheer went up from all the animals. Now they could sit down. They stayed for a long time and enjoyed the huge feast.

When the feast was over, the hippo kept his promise. He took his seven sisters and went to the river. Ever since that day, they have always lived in the water. At night, they come on shore to feed. But you never find a hippo on the land in the daytime. ❧

The *Dog* and *His* **Shadow**

Once there was a big dog. When he got a bone, he always hid it. He never gave a bit to any other dog.

If he saw a little dog with a bone he would say, "Bow-wow! Give me that bone!" Then he would take the bone.

One day, he took a bone from a little dog. "The little dog shall not find this bone," he said. "I will take it far away. I will go across the brook and hide it."

So the big dog ran to the brook. There was a bridge over the brook. The dog ran out onto the bridge. He looked down into the water and thought he saw another dog there. He thought the dog had a bone, too.

"I will take that bone," said the big dog. "Then I shall have two bones."

"Bow-wow!" said the big dog. When he did, his own bone fell out of his mouth. It fell into the brook. The big dog could not get it out.

There was not a dog in the water at all! The big dog had seen his own shadow.

The *Dog* and the *Wolf*

There once was a Wolf so skinny that he was nearly dead with hunger. He met a Dog who lived in a house in town.

The Dog saw that the Wolf was near death. "Dear Wolf," said the Dog, "your wild life will be the end of you. Why not work as I do, and get your food given to you each day?"

"I would be willing to try anything," said the Wolf, "if I could just get a place to live and something to eat."

"I can take care of that for you," said the Dog. "Come with me to my master and you can share my work."

As the Wolf and Dog made their way to the town, the Wolf saw that the hair on the Dog's neck was worn very thin.

"Dear Dog," said the Wolf. "Why is the hair on your neck worn so thin that your skin shows?"

"Oh, it's nothing. Don't worry about that," said the Dog. "That is just the place where my master puts the collar on my neck each night. After supper, I am chained. You will get used to it."

"Is that what it costs to eat every day?" said the Wolf. "Then good-bye, friend Dog. I would rather starve and be free."

The Boy Who Cried "Wolf"

Once a little boy was sent to take care of a large flock of sheep. His father said, "If a wolf comes to the pasture you must cry, 'Wolf! Wolf!' Then the men who are working in the field will come and drive him away."

For many days, no wolf came.

One day, the little boy thought that he would have some fun. So he cried to the men, "Wolf! Wolf!"

"Where? Where?" cried the men, as they ran to the pasture.

The boy laughed and said, "There is no wolf. I called to you for fun."

The men went back to their work. They did not like the boy's fun.

Two or three times, the boy called the men to the pasture. Each time, the men ran to drive away the wolf and found no wolf there.

At last, one day, a wolf came to the pasture. "Help! Help! A wolf! A wolf!" cried the boy.

This time, the men did not run to help him. They said, "He is having fun. We will not go."

The wolf killed one of the sheep and carried it to his den.

And the boy never called to the men in fun again. ✺